Wuff wuf.

C000076940

Speed Sounds

Consonants *Ask children to say the sounds.*

f	l	m	n	r	s	v	z	sh	(th)	ng
(ff)						ve				(nk)

b	c	d	g	h	j	p	qu	t	w	x	y	ch
	k											
	(ck)											

Vowels *Ask children to say the sounds in and out of order.*

a	e	i	o	u

Each box contains one sound but sometimes more than one grapheme.
*Focus graphemes for this story are **circled**.*

Ditty 1   Wuff wuff

Story Green Words

Ask children to read the words first in Fred Talk and then say the word.

has   black   thin

fat   wuff

Ask children to read the root first and then the whole word with the suffix.

pup → pups

Red Words
Ask children to practise reading the word.

my

Wuff wuff

Introduction
In this story we meet a dog and her pups. Let's see
what they are like!

my dog has got 4 pups

a big pup...

a black pup...

a thin pup...

and a fat pup

wuff wuff

Ditty 2 Help

Story Green Words

Ask children to read the words first in Fred Talk and then say the word.

soft	sand	have	quick
nap	nip	flat	pink
crab	help		

Red Words *Ask children to practise reading the words.*

I   the

7

Help

Introduction

Do you like going to the beach? The girl in this story has fun at the beach, but then she has a surprise...

I sit on the soft sand

I have a quick nap

nip nip

a flat pink crab

help help

Ditty 3   The big match

Story Green Words

Ask children to read the words first in Fred Talk and then say the word.

kick   back   net

clap   win

Ask children to read the root first and then the whole word with the suffix.

red → reds

Red Words
Ask children to practise reading the words.

the   of

11

The big match

Introduction

This is a story about a game of football. Can the red team win?

a man...

a big kick...

12

it is in the back of the net

clap clap clap

the reds win

Questions to talk about

Read out each question and ask children to TTYP (turn to your partner) and discuss.

Ditty 1

How many pups does the dog have?

What do the pups look like?

Tell me about a dog you know.

Ditty 2

What does the girl do after sitting on the sand?

What happens to the girl whilst she is napping?

What do you like doing at the seaside?

Ditty 3

What happens when the man kicks the ball?

Which team wins?

What is your favourite game?

Speedy Green Words

Ask children to practise reading the words across the rows, down the columns and in and out of order clearly and quickly.

got	dog	big	it
and	sit	man	is